CAMERON MACKINTOSH
IN ASSOCIATION WITH
THE WEST YORKSHIRE PLAYHOUSE PRESENTS

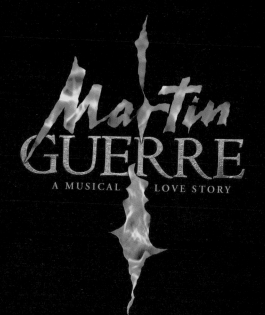

Martin GUERRE

A MUSICAL LOVE STORY

FRANCE
1560
ARTIGAT

A QUIET VILLAGE NEAR THE SPANISH BORDER
IS NOT YET TOUCHED BY THE RELIGIOUS WARS
THAT ARE TEARING FRANCE APART.

MEANWHILE FAR NORTH OF ARTIGAT
A BATTLE IS RAGING BETWEEN THE CATHOLICS
AND THE PROTESTANTS.

ACT I

On a battlefield, Martin Guerre, weary after so many years of fighting with the Catholic army, is consoled by his only friend, Arnaud du Thil. Moved by Arnaud's concern, Martin confides in him the story of his childhood.

Seven years earlier, in his home village of Artigat, the villagers are preparing for a very important day. Pierre Guerre, a wealthy landowner, has arranged that his reluctant young nephew, Martin, should marry Bertrande, the daughter of his close friend Madame de Rols. Everyone rejoices except Guillaume, Bertrande and Martin's childhood friend who is secretly in love with Bertrande. A few months later the celebration turns sour; Bertrande is not pregnant and Artigat has been hit by a freak deluge which threatens to destroy the new crop. In a village rife with religious superstition Guillaume has no trouble in convincing his fellow villagers that God has turned his back on Artigat because Bertrande's womb is now as barren as the land. They believe the lack of conception has invited Satan into their midst.

Martin Guerre soon becomes the scapegoat for the whole community and he is ritually beaten by the Priest, Father Dominic, in an exorcism ceremony. Hurt in his body and heart he takes the unusual risk of leaving his wife and family to start another life.

On the Battlefield – 1560. Arnaud, astounded by this revelation, still urges Martin to go back home, after so many years, and find out what his own feelings towards Bertrande and his own people are. Full of gratitude Martin decides that indeed the day has come for him to make the journey back to his past. But a sudden attack from the Protestant army cuts short his plans. As he is shielding Arnaud he himself is stabbed. Having saved Arnaud's life he is left for dead on the battlefield.

Meanwhile, in Artigat, Bertrande is under huge pressure from the villagers to give up her hope for Martin's return and to marry Guillaume. The only people who offer any comfort to her are Catherine and Andre, two of a tiny community of Protestants worshipping secretly in Artigat.

BERTRANDE

COSTUME ILLUSTRATIONS REPRODUCED BY
KIND PERMISSION OF ANDREANE NEOFITOU.
MASKS BY KIND PERMISSION OF JOHN NAPIER.

Artigat is now suffering a terrible drought at the end of a never-ending summer. Just as the village blamed Martin for the deluge seven years earlier, they now attribute the drought to Bertrande's unholy behaviour. They believe her refusal to marry and to procreate has angered God and that He is sending fires from the sky as a punishment. At her lowest point of despair Benoit, the village idiot, announces that a young man has arrived looking for Bertrande.

MARTIN GUERRE

Benoit was in the fields with his friend, Louison, a scarecrow, when the stranger appeared. As if by a miracle, a thunder clap is heard for the first time in months and soon the name of Martin Guerre is on everyone's lips. The newcomer, Arnaud du Thil, who has only travelled so far to bring Bertrande the news of Martin's death, is hailed as the prodigal son before he is able to say who he really is.

However, as soon as he is alone with Bertrande, Arnaud confesses the truth. But as he is about to leave he realises that the villagers won't let their saviour desert them. He has already done too much for them. They want him to stay.

ARNAUD DU THIL

Bertrande and Arnaud start living together in a strange distant relationship in separate rooms, getting closer as Arnaud soon becomes the second in command to his 'uncle', Pierre. Meanwhile, the Protestant order has quietly grown within Artigat and Bertrande has joined in their clandestine worship.

When Arnaud and Bertrande eventually consummate their growing love, she tells him her secret and takes him to witness a Protestant service for himself. Guillaume, whose love for Bertrande is as potent as ever, spies on the service and realises he has the opportunity to dispose of 'Martin'. He also knows that the child that Bertrande is carrying will be a Protestant child who will taint the blood of the Guerres.

After denouncing what he saw to Pierre Guerre, and thinking that he would now be given Bertrande as his wife, he incites the village to purge the leader of the Protestants in their midst. Just as he is threatening to kill Martin, Benoit, the village idiot, believing it will save Martin, reveals the secret he has held since his first encounter with the stranger. "He is not Martin Guerre". In the face of such a huge revelation the village is split into two camps: the Catholics who despise 'Martin' and the secret Protestants, who support him. On the orders of Pierre Guerre, Arnaud is arrested to be tried.

What no one knows is that the wounded Martin has survived his near fatal injury and is on his way back to Artigat.

ACT II

Arnaud, still claiming to be Martin, is brought before the court to stand trial for his deception. A succession of witnesses appear before the court until the central witness, Benoit, confuses the Judge even further. Bertrande, when called, speaks movingly of the man she loves, but avoids declaring his name. While the Judge retires to consider the case, the Villagers are divided.

The hate intensifies between Catholics and Protestants, people from the same village, once part of a close community. They now examine their consciences and look once again for the ultimate scapegoat that would return God's favours to Artigat.

Just before the Judge is about to dismiss the case through lack of evidence, a last minute witness asks to be heard. Martin Guerre is finally back home. He has travelled from the far North of France and on the way he has heard about an imposter having taken his name and his life in his own village.

Now the Judge pronounces his verdict. Arnaud du Thil's fate is left to Martin's judgement while Bertrande Guerre will obviously go back to her husband as she has never legally ceased to be his wife. The community is torn even further apart by this verdict. The Catholics, especially Guillaume, expected Arnaud to be hanged. The Protestants feel betrayed by Arnaud's deception, however fond they were of the man.

However, they all, except for Guillaume, look at Martin as their potential new saviour but he has no such intention. The anger from his early years is still very much alive. Guillaume seizes the moment as his last chance to save Bertrande from the evil that he believes has perverted her soul, and to lead a crusade against the Protestants. Guillaume is quickly supported by his fervent followers and Andre becomes their first victim. He is rescued at the last minute by his wife Catherine and their Protestant friends, all incensed and ready to fight. In the eruption of violence the innocent Benoit, carrying his Louison, is the Catholics' second victim. They call Louison a Protestant and break her to pieces.

Meanwhile, Bertrande is at
the jail reassuring Arnaud that
she will always love him.
Martin suddenly enters the jail
and the three of them confront
their feelings, dreams and hopes
about one another. Finally,
in the name of their friendship,
Martin decides to let them
both go free.

Guillaume and his followers
arrive at the jail to seize Arnaud
and see that justice is done.
They see Martin setting Arnaud
and Bertrande free. Guillaume
is incensed by the sight.

Artigat begins to burn.
The Protestants and Catholics
fight a bloody battle. During the
heat of the fight Father Dominic
is accidentally stabbed by Andre.
Father Dominic dies in Andre's
arms. Everyone freezes in terror
and panic. Guillaume, driven
to the edge of sanity, seizes
Bertrande and puts a knife
against her throat. Arnaud tries
to speak to Guillaume while
Martin moves towards him, both
saying "I'm Martin Guerre".
Finally Arnaud takes the thrust
of the knife that was intended
for Martin. Arnaud falls.
Before Guillaume can reach
Martin, Benoit arrives and beats
Guillame's head with a large piece
of wood left from Louison's body.
Whilst most of the villagers kneel
around Father Dominic's corpse,
Arnaud is dying in Bertrande's
arms. Pierre and all the Villagers
are in shock.

The dying Arnaud renews
his friendship vow to Martin
and gives his unborn child to the
safekeeping of Martin. In the
name of their friendship, Martin
makes Arnaud's eulogy in front
of the villagers and speaks of
their communal responsibility for
all that has happened. He speaks
with an understanding of life and
love he has learnt from his friend.

ALAIN BOUBLIL
BOOK & LYRICS

CLAUDE-MICHEL SCHÖNBERG
MUSIC & BOOK

STEPHEN CLARK
LYRICS

THIS BOOK © COPYRIGHT 1998
BOUBERG MUSIC LIMITED / WISE PUBLICATIONS
ORDER NO.MF10119
ISBN 0-7119-7324-5

RIGHTS OF DRAMATIC PERFORMANCE FOR
ALL COUNTRIES OF THE WORLD
ADMINISTERED BY CAMERON MACKINTOSH (OVERSEAS) LIMITED,
1 BEDFORD SQUARE, LONDON WC1B 3RA.
TELEPHONE: 0171-637 8866. FAX: 0171-436 2683.

PRINT RIGHTS FOR THE UNITED KINGDOM & EIRE
ADMINISTERED BY MUSIC SALES LIMITED,
8/9 FRITH STREET, LONDON W1V 5TZ.
TELEPHONE: 0171-434 0066. FAX: 0171-439 2848.

SONGBOOK ARRANGED AND EDITED BY STEPHEN COLEMAN.
MUSIC PREPARATION BY DAKOTA MUSIC SERVICE.
COVER & LOGO DEVICE DESIGN BY DEWYNTERS PLC.
COVER DESIGN COPYRIGHT ©
CAMERON MACKINTOSH (OVERSEAS) LIMITED.
PRINTED IN THE UNITED KINGDOM.

EXCLUSIVE DISTRIBUTORS:
MUSIC SALES LIMITED,
8/9 FRITH STREET, LONDON W1V 5TZ.
MUSIC SALES PTY LIMITED,
120 ROTHSCHILD AVENUE, ROSEBERY, NSW 2018, AUSTRALIA.

LIVE WITH SOMEBODY YOU LOVE

MUSIC BY

CLAUDE-MICHEL SCHÖNBERG

LYRICS BY

ALAIN BOUBLIL & STEPHEN CLARK

For Solo version: soloist should sing top line and make bars marked * instrumental.

9

10

YOUR WEDDING DAY

MUSIC BY
CLAUDE-MICHEL SCHÖNBERG

LYRICS BY
ALAIN BOUBLIL & STEPHEN CLARK

15

I'M MARTIN GUERRE

MUSIC BY
CLAUDE-MICHEL SCHÖNBERG

LYRICS BY
ALAIN BOUBLIL & STEPHEN CLARK

17

Guerre, fath-er I'm brave, and from your grave you'll keep me strong.

Yes, I'm Mar-tin Guerre, for they will learn when I re-turn that I be-

long. Soon_____ you____ will see_____ that

I can choose to___ be free. They all look for some-one to

22

WITHOUT YOU AS A FRIEND

MUSIC BY
CLAUDE-MICHEL SCHÖNBERG

LYRICS BY
ALAIN BOUBLIL & STEPHEN CLARK

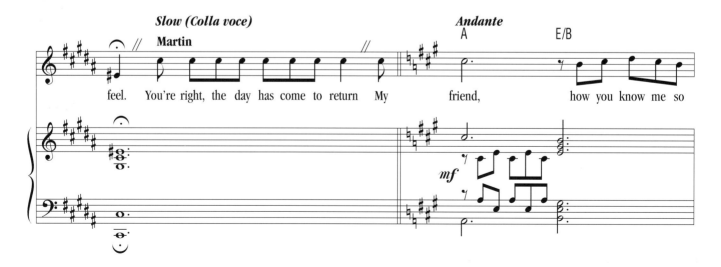

tend? Where would I be with-out you as a friend?_____ My

friend,_____ our lives are in God's hands now,_____ per-haps we're the luck-iest of

men. The life_____ you left be-longs to you now._____ I

hope one day we'll meet a-gain..._____

26

HOW MANY TEARS?

MUSIC BY
CLAUDE-MICHEL SCHÖNBERG

LYRICS BY
ALAIN BOUBLIL & STEPHEN CLARK

can - dle in_____ his name._____

Gently   *cedez*

How ma-ny tears though the years can I cry?   How ma-ny prayers to the   Lord must I

try? Still the pain tears at my   bro-ken heart.   Some-times I feel   I was cursed from the start.

Piu Mosso

All   I could hold,   all   I could see,   so   full of pro - mise,

30

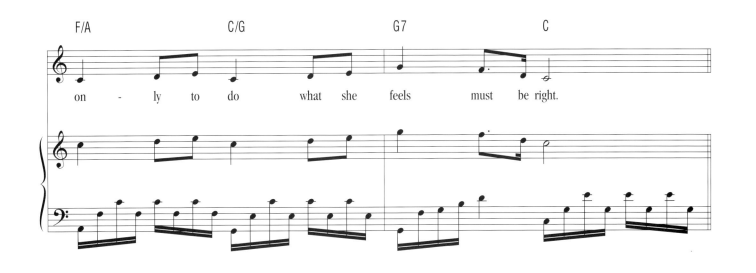

on - ly to do what she feels must be right.

Some - times I won - der if some-one hears. Why must I live through

so ma - ny tears?

WELCOME TO THE LAND

MUSIC BY
CLAUDE-MICHEL SCHÖNBERG

LYRICS BY
ALAIN BOUBLIL & STEPHEN CLARK

33

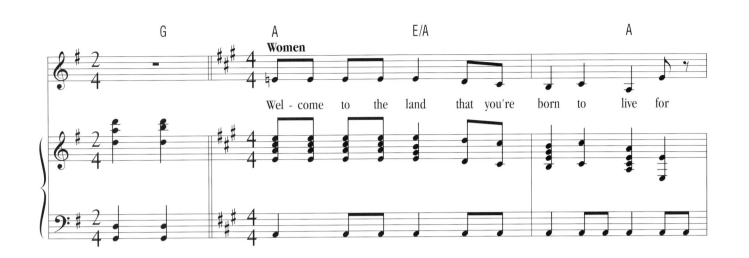

pray it will stay as good Cath' - lic land.

pray it will stay as good Cath' - lic land.

38

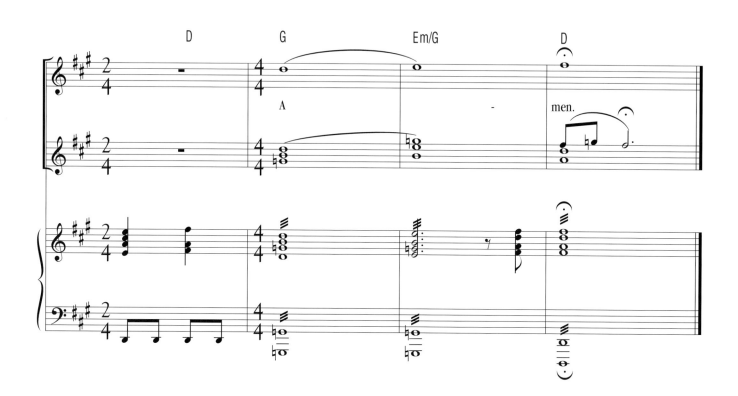

A - men.

DON'T

MUSIC BY
CLAUDE-MICHEL SCHÖNBERG

LYRICS BY
ALAIN BOUBLIL & STEPHEN CLARK

39

40

I hear each word you say,

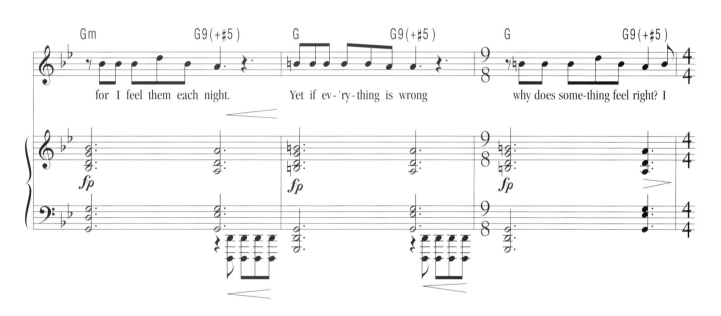

for I feel them each night. Yet if ev-'ry-thing is wrong why does some-thing feel right? I

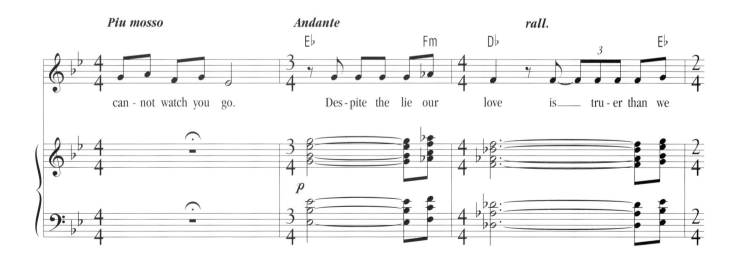

can - not watch you go. Des-pite the lie our love is___ tru - er than we

43

44

THE HOLY FIGHT

MUSIC BY
CLAUDE-MICHEL SCHÖNBERG

LYRICS BY
ALAIN BOUBLIL & STEPHEN CLARK

45

48

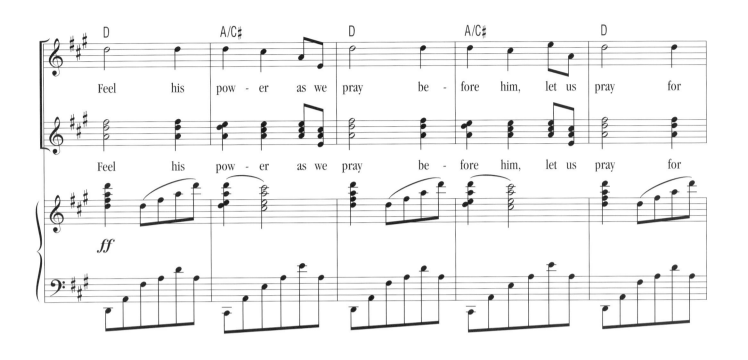

Feel his pow-er as we pray be-fore him, let us pray for

Feel his pow-er as we pray be-fore him, let us pray for

ff

guid - ance for the ho - ly fight.

guid - ance for the ho - ly fight.

ff

THE DAY HAS COME

MUSIC BY
CLAUDE-MICHEL SCHÖNBERG

LYRICS BY
ALAIN BOUBLIL & STEPHEN CLARK

51

52

53

Bbm   Bbm/Eb   *rit.*   Eb

make   is the love we'll make to - ge - ther___ all our

Ab   Eb/Ab **Guillaume**

Now the day has come, I will have her at

lives. The day has come   And there's

54

Db/Ab   Ab **Pierre**

last!   Who - e - ver he is, this man must be

no - thing in the world to change the love we know.

55

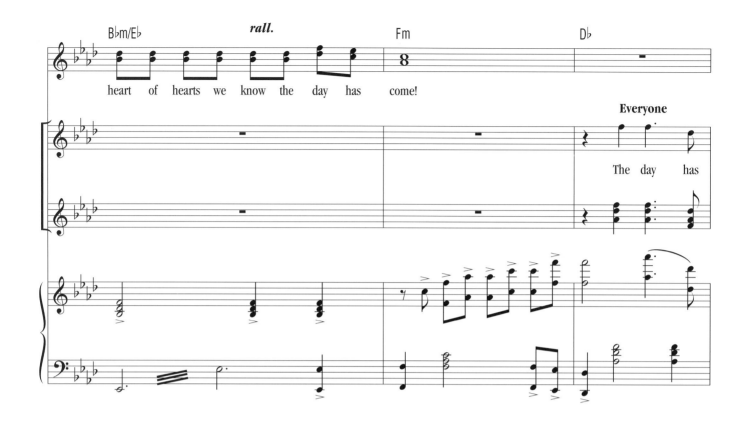

heart of hearts we know the day has come!

Everyone

The day has

56

come   it is judge-ment day, O lord the day has   come.

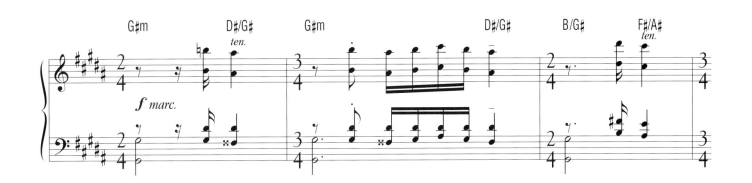

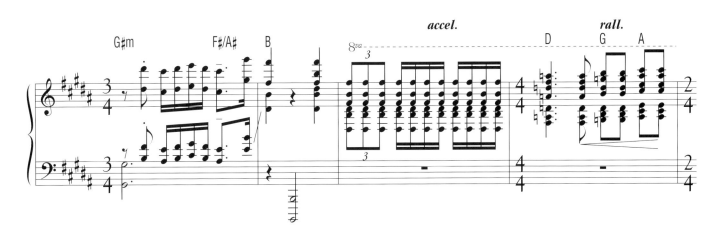

IF YOU STILL LOVE ME

MUSIC BY
CLAUDE-MICHEL SCHÖNBERG
LYRICS BY
ALAIN BOUBLIL & STEPHEN CLARK

59

Right from the first kiss, right from the

dawn, we would have felt this... The

faith that's found when trust is won, we would have known the heat that shows when

love's be-gun in the sun-light. If you still

60

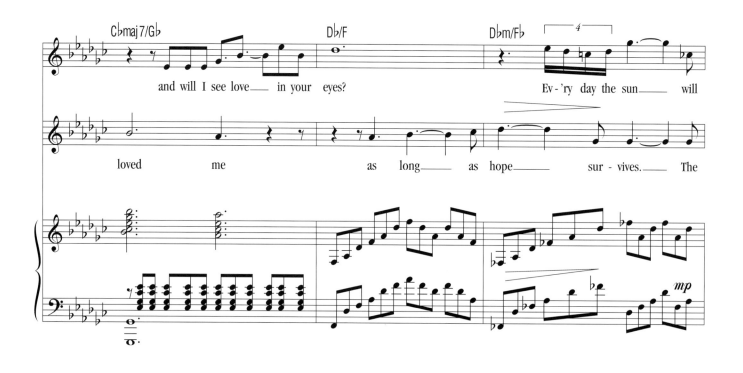

and will I see love—— in your eyes?

loved   me

Ev - 'ry day the sun—— will

as long—— as hope—— sur - vives.—— The

62

rise.——

and if   love—— ne - ver fades—— or for -

sun   should not rise   on re - grets

and if   love—— ne - ver fades—— or for -

WHO?

MUSIC BY
CLAUDE-MICHEL SCHÖNBERG

LYRICS BY
ALAIN BOUBLIL & STEPHEN CLARK

64

65

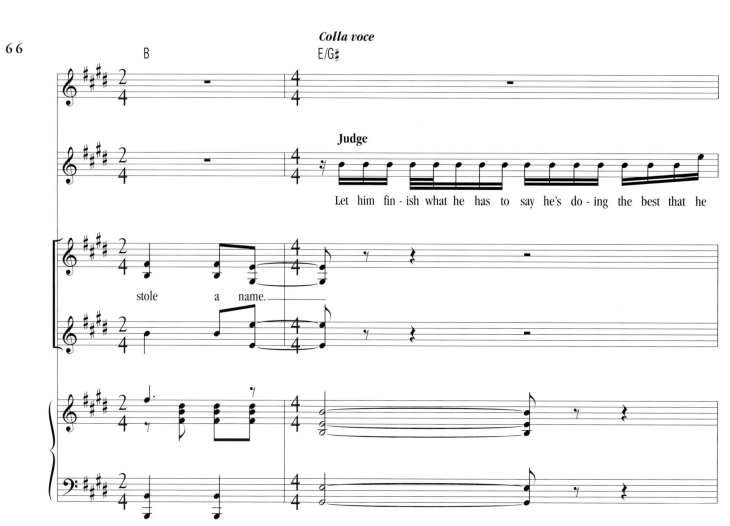

66

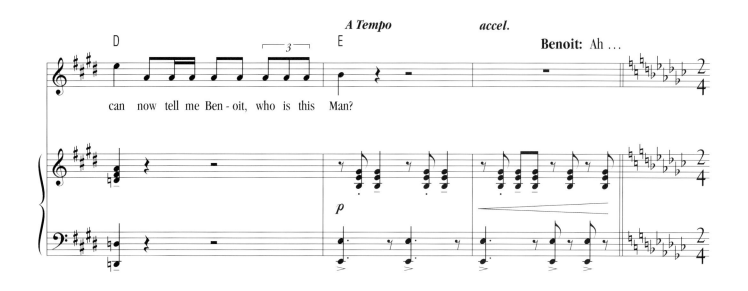

know that's not my name   see, it's strange   names can al-ways change   yet I'm stIll the same.___

Moderato come prima

Who can say why Loui-son has such   beau-ti-ful hair?

Can I know who he is if i'm   not Mar-tIn Guerre?___   Who?   He's who?   Who

poco accel.

The Whole Village

Who?   Who?

Meno Mosso

D   Gb/Db   Bm   Bbm

have ev - 'ry - one of you thrown out of court if this tur - moil hap - pens once more

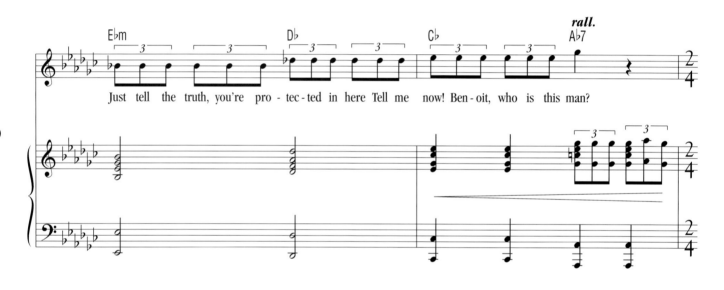

Ebm   Db   Cb   rall. Ab7

Just tell the truth, you're pro - tec - ted in here Tell me now! Ben - oit, who is this man?

Benoit   Gb/Db   Gb

Who? He's who you all want him to be for you.

ALL THAT I LOVE

MUSIC BY
CLAUDE-MICHEL SCHÖNBERG

LYRICS BY
ALAIN BOUBLIL & STEPHEN CLARK

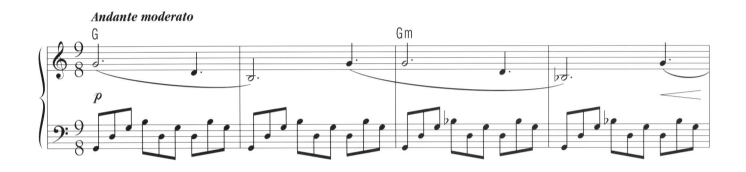

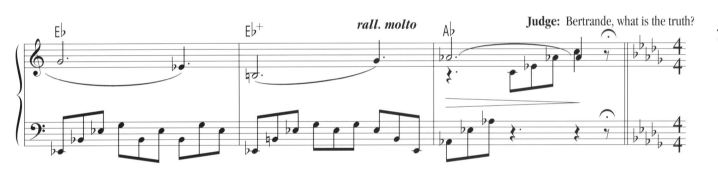

It is ea-sy to say, just as night be-comes day. The

truth's here be-fore me for All that I love, all that I know In

God's name I swear this is the man I gave my life to. All that I love,

all that I trust is here to stay be-side me, and the child that will bear his name. I

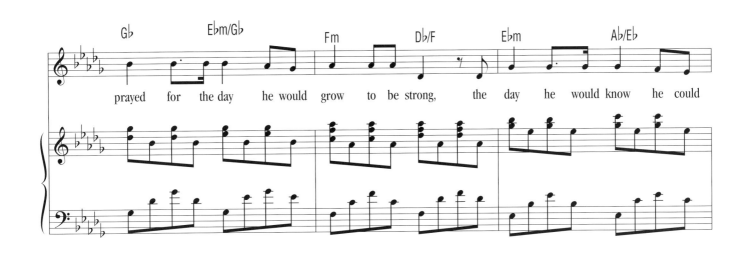

prayed for the day he would grow to be strong, the day he would know he could

love and be-long. He an-swered my prayers who can say love is wrong?

All that I need, all that I've planned re-turned to his land and made my life worth li-ving.

JUSTICE WILL BE DONE

MUSIC BY
CLAUDE-MICHEL SCHÖNBERG

LYRICS BY
ALAIN BOUBLIL & STEPHEN CLARK

75